Myth
or
Mystery?

Contents

The Monster of Lake Iliamna

A traditional Athabascan legend from Alaska

Long ago, in a land far to the north, a father, mother, and son lived beside a lake so large, it seemed to flow into the sky.

The small family lived well in their lakeside home. The old man caught moose, caribou, and fish. There was also small game, and in the summer there were berries of all kinds. As the son grew into a strong hunter, the father and mother felt they had everything they could ever want.

Life was good until one summer day when the harsh snows had stopped and the wind was still. The son was in his canoe, hunting some caribou that were in the water, where they were hiding from hungry mosquitoes.

The son quickly killed a caribou. But, as he loaded the animal into his canoe, the lake waters began to froth angrily. He dropped the caribou and tried to paddle away. Then suddenly, his canoe was sucked into the deep lake, and he disappeared from sight.

Although the father and mother searched and searched for their son, they never saw him again. They knew he had been captured by the monster that lived in the lake.

The father vowed he would kill the monster, once and for all. All summer and fall, he cut down the trees surrounding the huge lake. And that winter, he pushed the trees onto the frozen lake.

There were so many trees, that they covered the lake like a heavy blanket.

When spring finally came and the ice melted, the father set fire to the floating trees. After four days, the huge lake started to steam. After eight days, it began to boil.

Suddenly, a sound like thunder split the air. In the waters below where the father and mother waited, the burning trees started to move. A giant, snake-like monster, more massive than a herd of one hundred caribou, threw itself out of the water and onto the beach.

The father had vowed that he would kill the monster that had taken his son, and he had done it.

Or Had He?

People who live around Lake Iliamna, the largest lake in Alaska, still see enormous, snake-like shapes swimming in the lake.

Some think the monster is a herd of seals, or a giant fish called a sturgeon.

The problem is that sturgeons don't match the description of what people see. While sturgeons can be more than twenty feet long, they swim only in the deepest parts of the lake – not along the surface.

Lake Iliamna does seem like the perfect place for a monster. If a monster lives there, maybe it thinks so, too.

Monsters of the Land

The Bigfoot File

"...and when the family looked out the window of their cabin to see what their dog was barking at, they saw a big, hairy creature running into the forest."

"Well, Kathy, it looks as though Bigfoot is on the loose again – or should I say, the Bigfoot myth is on the loose again?" the newscaster said, chuckling.

The television screen went dark, and Daisy walked into the kitchen. "Hey, Grandpa! There was this weird story on the news about some monster running around in the mountains!" she said with a laugh. "Are we supposed to believe that? How silly do they think we are?"

"Oh, Daisy, I wouldn't laugh about that if I were you. Old Bigfoot doesn't come out often, but many of the folks who live around here are pretty sure he's real," Grandpa said.

Daisy frowned. Her week at her grandparents' cabin in the woods of northern Oregon had just begun, and her grandpa was already teasing her. Before she could start to object, he got up and pulled a dust-covered shoebox out of the hall closet. He smiled and said, "I have something to show you. Could you help me sort this out?"

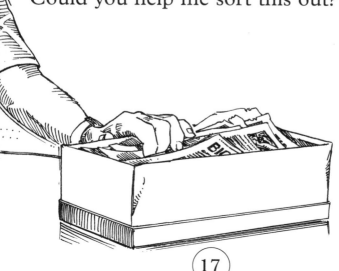

As he lifted the top off the box, some newspaper clippings and photographs came spilling out. Right there on top was a yellowed article with a big, bold headline.

Bigfoot Sighted?

BRITISH COLUMBIA. The creat
A railway engineer and to be 4 feet

"Grandpa, what is all this stuff?" Daisy asked as she started flipping through the articles and photographs.

"Oh, just records of some local sightings of our furry friend. My dad started this file in the 1920s when he was prospecting for gold in these mountains. I've been adding to it ever since he gave it to me."

Bigfoot Sighted?

BRITISH COLUMBIA. A railway engineer and crew encountered an unusual creature during their weekly train run. The creature, a hairy, gorilla-like animal, was seen running along the cliffs near the tracks.

The engineer saw what he thought was a man sleeping next to the railroad tracks. He blew the whistle to stop the train, and the train squealed to a halt. The "man" jumped up, made a barking sound, and then began to climb a steep, rocky hillside.

The creature was said to be 4 feet, 7 inches tall and weigh 127 pounds. It looked like a man except that its entire body was covered with long black hair.

Daisy was finding the whole thing very hard to believe. She held up one article titled "Why Did Bigfoot Cross the Road?"

"Grandpa, I don't get it," Daisy said. "If all these people think that they've seen this Bigfoot, why doesn't the rest of the world know about it?"

Why Did Bigfoot Cross the Road?

CALIFORNIA.

A local couple was startled while driving in the mountains last night, when their headlights lit upon a tall figure crossing the road in front of them.

Asking her husband to slow down so she could get a better look, the woman thought what she was seeing was a very tall person wearing a full-length fur coat. She estimated the figure to be more than 7 feet tall, and it appeared to be completely covered with short, black hair.

"It was so strange. He had this big pointy head," the woman said.

"He turned around slowly. He was looking right at our car!"

The couple doubts that what they saw was simply a man playing a trick. "I tell you, this furry thing was a whole lot bigger than any normal guy," the man said. "I can't begin to figure out why anyone would think it was a good idea to dress up in an ape costume and walk across a highway at midnight."

Local park rangers are trying to decide what the couple saw. While some think it could have been a bear, others insist that bears would never walk along a highway on their hind feet.

"Well, Daisy, I think more people know about this than you might think. There are reports of creatures like this in Asia, Australia, South America, Africa, and Japan. Somewhere around here, I have some stories from an old Nootkas Indian who used to live nearby. I wrote down the stories as he told them to me. His tribe has countless legends about the local 'wild men' that they call Sasquatch."

Daisy couldn't believe what she was hearing. "But isn't there any real proof? What about skeletons? How can people believe this stuff if they've never found any evidence like that?"

"Well, if you think about it, that makes sense, too. Because of natural scavengers, people rarely find skeletons of black bears or wildcats, and we know they exist. And some people think Bigfoot is related to humans.

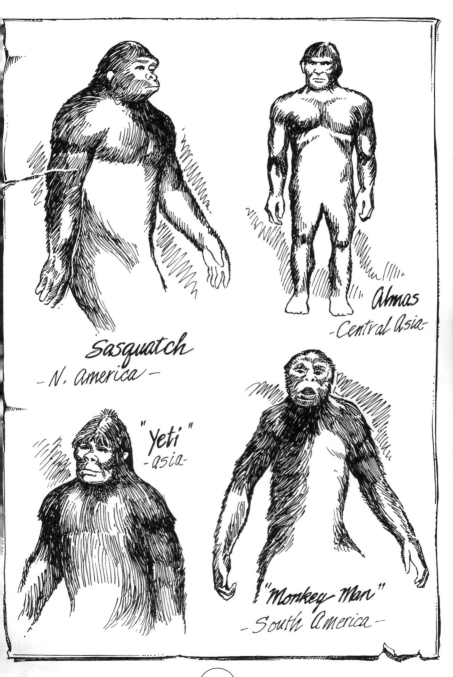

Sasquatch
- N. America -

Almas
- Central Asia -

"Yeti"
- Asia -

"Monkey-Man"
- South America -

So maybe it would bury its dead," Grandpa said.

"Grandpa, you sound as though you believe this. Don't tell me you've seen one of these monsters," Daisy said.

Without saying a word, Grandpa pulled out an article, smoothed it out, and handed it to her. Daisy took it from him and started to read.

Proof at Last? Loggers Find Giant Footprints

OREGON.

A team of loggers working in a nearby forest may have found proof that Sasquatch is still roaming the hills west of Portland.

The crew leader first saw a trail of huge footprints near his truck a month ago. The tracks came from out of the forest, and it looked as if something had been examining the chainsaws.

When the loggers found more of the enormous footprints yesterday, they took several pictures of them and also made plaster casts of the prints.

Scientists examining all of the evidence say that the footprints appear to have been made by a foot about $1\frac{1}{2}$ feet long, and 6 inches wide. The depth of the prints indicates that they were made by something that weighs well over 500 pounds.

Daisy finished the article and looked up at her grandpa. "It sounds as if they really did see something, but how do you know those prints weren't fakes?"

Grandpa gave her a serious look, and then he said, "I know they weren't fakes, because I was a member of that construction team. Some people may get a kick out of faking tracks or wearing gorilla costumes and parading around in the woods to get attention, but I don't think that's what happened this time."

"Weren't you scared? I don't know if I like the idea of staying up here if there is some sort of huge thing running around outside," Daisy said. "Some of these stories make this creature sound pretty mean." She pointed to a very old, faded article titled "Monster Ape Attacks Miners."

Monster Ape Attacks Miners

WASHINGTON.

Four miners were attacked at their mining claim in a canyon near Mt. Saint Helens. The workers had seen enormous footprints near their camp several times before, but they never felt as if they were in any danger.

Then, while eating his lunch two days ago, one of the miners saw a tall, hairy creature walk along a trail high above the canyon. The miner fired three shots to scare the creature away from the area.

That night, the men were awakened by a loud thumping noise. They discovered that rocks were hitting the roof and walls of their cabin.

When the men went outside to discover who was throwing the stones, the stone-throwing stopped. However, it began again once the men went back in.

The next night, it happened again. And last night, as the stones continued to rain down on the cabin, the frightened men packed up their belongings and left.

Today, a search party that went into the canyon found huge rocks lying around the little cabin. The inside of the cabin had been torn to shreds.

"No," Grandpa said. "Most of the time, the stories talk about how gentle and shy Bigfoot is. I don't think those miners should have been shooting their guns and trying to frighten whatever they saw. I don't blame that Sasquatch for throwing rocks at them and destroying their cabin!" Then, Grandpa picked up a photo of his old hunting dog and smiled.

"Hey, that's Austin! Why is his picture in the box, Grandpa?" Daisy asked.

"Well, one time many years ago, Austin was missing for more than a week. I was sure something terrible had happened to him. Then early one morning, I heard some whining outside the door. I looked out and there was Austin, lying on the back porch. His leg was all chewed up, and it looked as if he had gotten caught in some sort of an animal trap." Grandpa took off his glasses and rubbed his eyes.

"I was so glad to see my dog, that it took me a few minutes to notice he had some big leaves wrapped around his hurt leg. It looked as if someone had given him first aid. He certainly couldn't have walked in that condition. Something had rescued my dog and carried him back to my house."

"Do you think it was Bigfoot?"

"Well," Grandpa said, "I'll never know for sure. What do you think?"

The Search for Kongamato

I can't believe it — I'm finally in Africa, and tomorrow I start on a search for an animal that many people believe died out more than 65 million years ago. I've read everything I can get my hands on about these monster birds, and even if I don't find a modern-day dinosaur, I think there must be something out there. Too many people have seen it. Too many tribes have stories about it. Too many intelligent people believe it's true. I will check my list one last time, and then it's off to bed. Tomorrow will be a long day.

We've been traveling through northwestern Zambia for five days now and have left the cities far behind. We are entering the lands of the Kaonde, who are a tribal people with a folklore rich in stories of the monster bird they call Kongamato. Today, my guides introduced me to a tribe member who says he has seen this creature. He described a giant, bloodthirsty bird that looks like a lizard with wings like a huge bat.

I showed him many pictures of
known animals, but he just shook his
head. Then, when I pulled out
a picture of a pterodactyl — a
prehistoric flying dinosaur — he
became excited and insisted that
it was the creature he had seen.

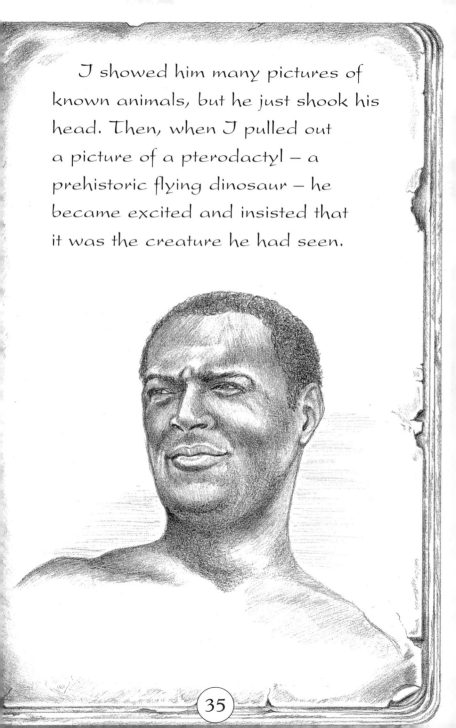

It's difficult to chase an animal that leaves no trace except for the stories of people who have seen it. Because of this, I've decided to look deep into the past to try to get an idea of what kind of life the monster bird would lead today.

If the monster bird really is a pterodactyl, we're looking for an animal that supposedly became extinct 65 million years ago, and that has a wingspan ranging from 36 to 40 feet!

Because pterodactyls fed on fish, lizards, and other vertebrates, our best bet is to stay close to the waterways, where there is an abundance of this kind of prey. I hope my theory works, for I would love to find out, once and for all, what is behind all of these different stories.

June 13

It is strange how the more things change, the more they stay the same. Tonight, while we were sitting around the fire, I started trading stories with my guides.

I told them about the legendary monster birds from back home. I described how Native Americans who used to live up and down the Mississippi River believed in the terrible Piasa bird. They carved and painted enormous pictures of the bird on cliffs along the river.

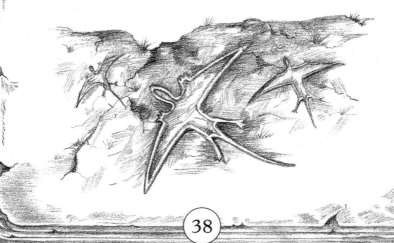

When I told my guides that
the Native Americans believed the
Piasa bird captured and carried
away humans to feed its young, the
guides nodded seriously. They said
this monster bird sounded very much
like their Kongamato. It seems
strange that two completely different
cultures, living so far apart, could
have stories of such similar creatures.

I am still
shaking from what
happened to me
earlier today.
What makes
everything even
worse is that
I think I may
have missed my
one and only chance to learn
about the monster bird.

This afternoon, when we were
preparing to climb a small butte that
stood in our path to the next river,
my guides suddenly got very
nervous and began softly chanting
under their breath.

When I asked what was wrong,
they said that Kongamato was
very close.

They were so afraid, that they refused to leave the safety of the jungle to climb up on the exposed rocks. I continued on my way, hoping they would eventually follow me to our next campsite.

I had just reached the top of the rocky butte when it happened. Everything seemed to be fine until I suddenly heard a tremendous swooshing sound. I was just turning around to see what all the commotion was about, when I heard a loud scream. The next thing I knew, something very hard and sharp hit the back of my head.

That's the last thing I remember. The next thing I knew, my guides were pulling me off of the exposed rocks, and down to the shelter of the undergrowth.

My guides tell me that I was attacked by Kongamato, but because I never saw what came at me, or what actually happened, I can't be sure. Despite my sore head, I'll continue my search tomorrow...

The Unicorn

During medieval times, many people believed in this animal, which looks like a white horse with blue eyes and a single horn sticking out of its forehead. The unicorn's horn was thought to have magical powers. Nobles often paid high prices for what they believed to be unicorn horns. In many fantasy books today, the unicorn continues to be a very popular character.

The Loch Ness Monster

For hundreds of years, people have told strange stories of an enormous, serpent-like monster that lives in a deep lake in the Scottish Highlands. There are more than 4,000 reports of sightings of this monster, and even a few photographs. However, no one has really proven what it is that lives in the lake.

The Lusca

Bahama Islanders tell terrifying tales of Lusca – a giant sea creature that is half giant squid and half giant octopus. Lusca is said to pull boats to the bottom of the ocean, and to leave huge round welts from its suckers on those who are lucky enough to escape its grasp.

My grandmother used to take me to see pictures of the terrifying Piasa bird that were carved in the cliffs above the Mississippi River. Even though these carvings are now gone, my memories of them are still strong. I get a chill when I imagine strange, monstrous animals living in our midst.

While I've never seen any of the monsters mentioned in this book, my friends tell me that I live with two of the worst monsters ever – my dogs, Basil and Stella!

Rebecca Weber

From the Illustrators

I have just moved to Denver from Chicago. *Myth or Mystery?* is my twentieth children's book.
I like illustrating for children because it reminds me of what a great time I had drawing as a child.

Sam Thiewes

I live in Colorado with my children, Paul and Nicolle. I would like to thank Roland Booth and Megan, Matt, and Rebecca Anderson for their help in illustrating this book.

Shawn Shea

I had a lot of fun illustrating my section of *Myth or Mystery?* I wondered what might happen next to the monsters or the people looking for them. I suppose that's a mystery, too!

Connie Marshall

ANOTHER TIME, ANOTHER PLACE

Cloudcatcher
Flags
The Dinosaur Connection
Myth or Mystery?
Where Did the Maya Go?
The Journal: Dear Future II

CONFIDENCE AND COURAGE

Imagine This, James Robert
Follow That Spy!
Who Will Look Out for Danny?
Fuzz and the Glass Eye
Bald Eagles
Cottle Street

SOMETHING STRANGE

My Father the Mad Professor
A Theft in Time: Timedetectors II
CD and the Giant Cat
Chocolate!
White Elephants and Yellow Jackets
Dream Boat

WHEN THINGS GO WRONG

The Long Walk Home
The Trouble with Patrick
The Kids from Quiller's Bend
Laughter Is the Best Medicine
Wild Horses
The Sunday Horse

Written by **Rebecca Weber**
Illustrated by **Sam Thiewes** ("The Monster of Lake Iliamna");
Shawn Shea ("The Bigfoot File"); and **Connie Marshall**
("In Search of Kongamato")
Edited by **Jennifer Waters**
Designed by **Mary C. Walker**

02 01 00 99 98 97
10 9 8 7 6 5 4 3 2 1

Distributed in the United States by
  Rigby
  a division of Reed Elsevier Inc.
  P.O. Box 797
  Crystal Lake, IL 60039-0797

Printed by Colorcraft, Hong Kong
ISBN: 1-57257-746-0